China Girl

by

David Belbin

Illustrated by Julia Page

First published in 2009 in Great Britain by
Barrington Stoke Ltd
18 Walker St, Edinburgh, EH3 7LP

www.barringtonstoke.co.uk

ISBN: 978-1-84299-664-5

Printed in Great Britain by Bell & Bain Ltd

A Note from the Author

The title of this book comes from a hit song. But the story has nothing to do with the song. This story is about first love. And it's about illegal immigrants. But mainly, I think, it's about choice.

Not everyone has choices. If you're poor, you don't have much choice. Some people break the law in order to escape being poor. They feel that's their only way out. Other people choose to do bad things because they are greedy. Greedy for money. Greedy for sex. Greedy for what they can get.

Every choice you make changes you. See what you think of the choices made by the people in this story.

For Martin Stannard

Contents

Chapter 1

Off Sick

I met her because I was off school sick. She came into my room.

"Sorry, sorry," she said.

"It's OK," I told her. My face turned red. She was the first girl to see me in my

underpants. She was small, pretty, Chinese.
Not much older than me. She backed out of
the room.

I got dressed and looked for her. She was
cleaning the loo. I tried to chat her up.

"What's your name?"

She gave me a funny look. "No English."

She bent over. Nice bum. I thought about
sneaking a feel. I've seen Dad do that.
Sometimes girls act like they like it. But my

dad's a big bloke, and rich. I'm skinny and only sixteen. I don't want to be like my dad. Except for the rich bit.

"Go way, please," the girl said. "They say no talking."

"Do you work for my dad?"

My dad runs a job agency.

"No understand."

"Bet you do, really." I smiled at her. "Have you been in this country long?"

"Not long." She smiled back. I'd caught her out.

****

Later, I asked Mum about her.

"She started last week," Mum said. "She does a lot in four hours."

"What's she called?"

"I don't know. She's one of your dad's girls. They come and go. I don't want you talking to her."

"Why not?"

"She's staff."

Chapter 2

Skiving Off

I couldn't stop thinking about the Chinese girl. I was in love. Or lust. Is there a difference? I had to see her again.

A week later, I skived off school. I put my best jeans on. I didn't want her to know I was still a schoolboy. I worked out what to say to her then went down into the kitchen.

She was cleaning the floor.

"What do you think of England?" I asked.

"OK."

"I'd like to visit your country. What part are you from?"

"Hunan Province," she told me.

"Do you have a boyfriend there?"

She didn't reply. But when I asked her name, she told me.

"Wang Yang Ling," she said.

"Can I call you 'Ling'? I like the way it sounds."

She nodded.

"I'm Ryan," I told her. "Where do you live now, Ling?"

She pretended not to understand.

"You can trust me." I still wasn't sure she understood.

"Told not to talk," she replied.

Ling let me talk to her while she polished the floor. Then we heard Mum come back. Ling looked alarmed. I winked at her. Then I left by the back door.

We shared a secret. It felt good. But I wanted to know more about Ling. So, later that day, I came back. I hung around at the end of our street. Then I followed her home.

On the way to the station, I nearly went up to Ling. But she might think I was a creep. So I hung back. Ling took a long tube ride and a longer walk. She stared at the floor all the way. She looked sad and didn't notice me at all.

Ling got off in an area I didn't know. I followed her down a street full of take-aways and taxi firms. She turned into an alley. From the alley, I heard footsteps on a fire escape. I saw a first floor door open and close. Now I knew where she lived.

A hand grabbed my arm.

"Hey, kid! What you doing round here?"

"Nothing," I told the young Chinese man. "Just passing."

"You want girl? Wrong place."

"OK," I said.

"Go now."

I should have gone home, but I didn't. I bought a bag of chips. Then I stood in the alley, waiting for Ling. I finished my chips and went to the fire escape. I went up.

The door on the first floor was locked. I climbed the fire escape. The second floor door had no handle, but wasn't fully shut. I pulled it open and looked inside. The room stank of sweat. The floor was full of people. Most were sleeping. All looked Chinese. I closed the door and left at once.

Chapter 3

Three Kisses

The next week, I went to school but left early. I waited until Mum went to the shops. Then I found Ling in the bathroom. She was more relaxed this week. She knew Mum wouldn't be back for a while. Her English was getting better too.

"Hi, Ryan. How are you?"

"Happy to see you. Are you well?"

"I am good," Ling told me.

"Do you like it here?"

"It is OK. I like London."

"What do you do when you're not here?"

She cleaned in other houses, she said.

"Do you have friends here?"

"A few."

"Do they clean too?"

"Some do. Some have other work. It pays much better. But it is not nice. You know what I mean?"

"Massage?" I asked.

She nodded and lowered her head. My dad's agency found people work in factories and shops. But the big money for pretty young Asian girls was in 'massage' parlours.

Sex work. I was too embarrassed to talk about this with Ling. Instead I asked if I could take a picture of her on my phone.

"OK."

I took a head shot. Then I got Ling to take off her work coat. Under it, she wore a 2008 Beijing Olympics T-shirt.

Ling giggled when she looked at the photos. Then she looked sad again.

"Do you send money home?"

"Not yet," she said. "Soon, if I work hard."

"I think you're really pretty," I said, and tried to kiss her. She ducked.

"Please." She took a step away. "No."

"Do you have a boyfriend at home?"

"No boyfriend."

"Let me be your boyfriend. Let me help you."

She gave me a look that was sad but grateful. When I tried to kiss her again, she let me. Then she pulled away.

"Will you show me where you come from?" I asked.

I led her to my room and put Google Earth on the internet. The screen seemed to shoot across oceans. Ling was excited. Soon we found her part of China. Hunan. I'd never heard of it.

"More people live in Hunan Province than in UK," Ling said. "There are thirteen cities in Hunan."

We tried to zoom in on her nearest city, Zhuzhou. I wanted to get a close look, like you can with London. But the picture broke up. Was China so big that Google didn't have time to take lots of photos? Whatever, Ling didn't seem to mind.

"Thank you," she said, and kissed me hard.

Then she saw the time on the computer display.

"I must work," she said. "Lot left to do."

I helped her clean the kitchen and the hall. Then I heard a car. Mum was back. I shouldn't be here. I kissed her one last time.

"When can I see you again?" I asked at the back door.

"Next week."

"I can't wait that long," I said. My heart was thumping. "Do you have a mobile?"

She shook her head.

"Next week, I promise, I'll get you one."

Chapter 4

Gone

Next week I bunked off school to see her again. I had a cheap pay-as-you-go ready for Ling. There was twenty quid credit on it. Only Ling wasn't there. It was a different Chinese girl. Older. A woman, really.

"Where's Ling?" I asked her.

But this woman spoke no English at all.

"What happened to our cleaner?" I asked Mum later.

"Has she gone?" Mum said, looking away from me. "I can't keep track of the people your dad employs."

At least I knew where she lived. On Saturday, I went there. I climbed the fire escape steps again. The room was full of people sleeping, like before. I called Ling's name. No reply. No one even stirred. I looked around. The room stank. Much worse than before. The sleepers were in bad shape. The men weren't shaved. The women had dirty clothes, messy hair. They looked like they'd just arrived.

I'm not stupid. I knew Ling was an illegal immigrant. That's why Mum wanted to keep me away from her. Dad sometimes uses illegals. He says everyone does. That night, when we were on our own, I asked him.

"What happened to our cleaner, Ling?"

"What's it to you?"

I couldn't think of an answer. I'm a crap liar.

"You have a thing for her?" Dad asked. "There are lots more where she came from. Wait until you're a bit older."

"But where did she go?" I asked.

"Girls like her soon work out where the real money is," he told me. I tried not to show how angry I was. I made up my mind:

I'd find Ling. I'd do whatever it took. I might need money to buy her time. So later, when Dad was asleep, I crept into his bedroom. I looked in his wallet. It was packed. I took three hundred quid. I knew he'd beat the crap out of me if he found out. I didn't care.

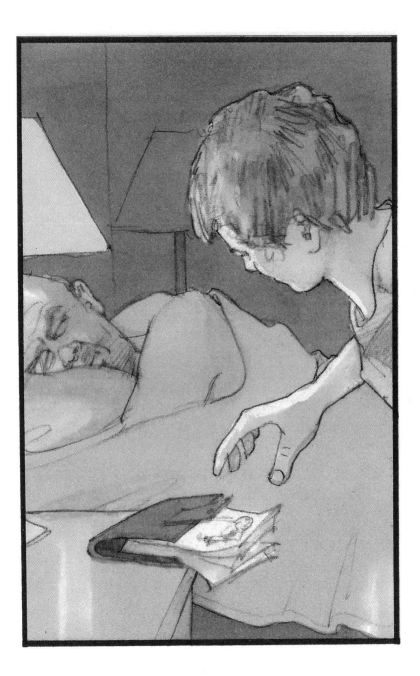

Chapter 5

The Boss

It was late Sunday morning when I got to the alley where Ling lived. I hung around for a while. Then I crept up the stairs. I pulled open the door. Empty. Inside, the floor was covered with thin, dirty mattresses. No clothes or bags, no personal stuff at all. Ling was gone. They'd all gone. I didn't know

what to do. Then I heard footsteps on the fire escape.

Nowhere to hide. I tried the inside door. Locked. In the corner of the room was a plastic shower curtain. I hid behind it. I expected to find a shower unit. There was only a toilet and a sink with one tap. Damp stains covered the walls and floor. I heard voices. Two men were speaking English, but their accents were Chinese.

"Twenty fit here." It was the guy who had warned me off. Room below, twenty more."

"Can they get out?"

"Door is watched. Room below locks on inside. Anyway, where they go? No money. No papers."

"Some of these people smart. Good English. Family. Can find good jobs. Don't want to pay what they owe. So put lock on door."

"Not safe. What if there's a fire?"

"Put lock on door."

"When by?"

"They come tonight. Midnight."

As the two men left, I took a look. The older guy was Dad's age. He must be the guy who brought Ling here. I thought about dialling 9-9-9. Not giving my name. *Want to know where forty illegals will be arriving tonight?* But you never go to the police. Dad taught me that as soon as I was old enough to understand.

When the footsteps faded, I hurried down into the alley. I wanted to know where the other room was.

I couldn't see the two men. I went back to the main road. After five minutes, I spotted the older man. He was going into an office with dark windows. I read the sign on the front. *Zhang Wang Kai: Accountant.*

I looked through the dark window. Suddenly the door opened. A hand reached out and grabbed me. I was yanked inside.

"You follow me," Wang said. "What you want?"

"Nothing."

"Why you follow me?"

"You came out of this room where I saw a girl," I told him. "A girl I like. Look."

I got out my phone and showed him the photo of Ling.

"You want this girl?"

"Yes."

"How you meet this girl? She not working long."

"She cleaned for us."

The man frowned. I worked out what he meant by *not working long*. Ling was in a massage parlour.

"When she work for you?" he asked.

"Until the week before last."

"You sure you don't know where she is now?"

"If I did, I'd be with her now."

"Wait."

He got out his mobile and made a call. "Come. Now."

A minute later, the young Chinese guy arrived. "This boy you saw three weeks ago?"

"Yes, Mr Wang."

Wang turned to me. "You went and looked inside room. You were seen." He turned to his side-kick. "Take him to boss."

"Aren't you the boss?" I asked Wang. He ignored me.

"Take him to boss. I phone to say you coming."

"OK," the side-kick said. He put me into a grey Ford Focus. We drove deeper into the city. What kind of a boss was in his office on a Sunday? I was sweating. I wished I hadn't followed Wang. I wished I'd phoned the police.

The car pulled up outside an office in Paddington. I knew this place. I knew who was inside. I got out of the car and started to run. Dad was already in the street. He grabbed my arm, so tight it hurt.

"So this is why you nicked that three hundred quid," he says. "If you wanted the girl so badly, why didn't you just say so?"

Then he took me inside and beat the hell out of me.

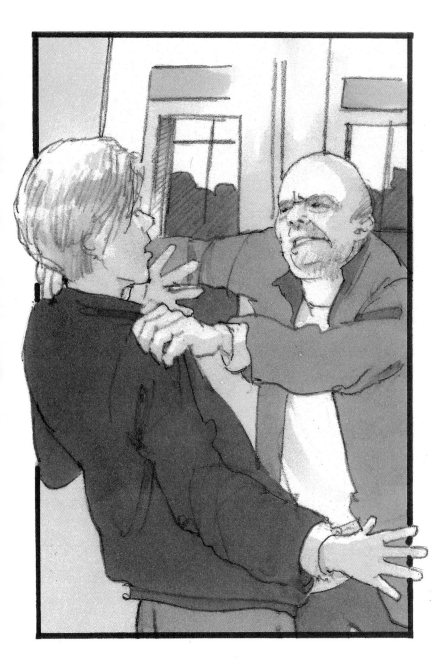

Chapter 6

My First Job

I should have guessed that Dad owned massage parlours. Mum knew. That was why she wouldn't let Ling talk to me. Mum knew what was going to happen to her. She was ashamed.

This is how it works. People leave poor countries in search of a better life. Dad chooses pretty girls fresh off the lorries. He gives them simple, badly paid work. Then he lets them settle in for a few weeks. They learn a bit of English and they find out how the world works. They owe a lot of money. They won't get that money by cleaning for less than the minimum wage. Other girls tell them that there's only one way to earn big money.

Ling didn't like it, but she did as she was told. I don't like it, but you don't diss the family business. Mum doesn't like it, but she likes the big house, the big cars, the long holidays.

I was meant to like the posh school I went to. But I didn't. I left after my GCSEs.

That was a year ago. When I got over the beating, I kept on at Dad about Ling. He wouldn't tell me where she was. It was months before I found out what happened.

Ling took the job Dad offered her in one of his massage parlours. She did what she

was told. Soon they thought she was broken
in. They let her go outside. And she did a
runner.

The people who smuggled her to the UK
were mad at Dad. She still owed them
thousands. So when I came looking for Ling,
Dad got really mad at me.

I've kept my eye out for Ling, but she got
away good. I haven't seen her again. Or
maybe I have. There are new girls every
month. After a while, it's hard to remember
who was who. When he attacked me, Dad

smashed up my phone with the photos of her. Would I know Ling if I saw her on the street? I can't be sure.

I work for my dad now. It was this or stack shelves in the supermarket. I want more from life than that. Dad's starting to trust me again. I collect the money from the massage parlours for him. Since I got my licence, I drive the girls around 24/7. I remember how I felt about Ling, so I look after them well.

Me and the girls, we have stuff in common. I hate my job. They hate theirs. I like them. Most of them seem to like me. Some even trust me. But I can't afford to trust them. If one runs away, I get into trouble. It doesn't happen often, though. Most are too scared to even try.

I know how they feel.

Barrington Stoke would like to thank all its readers for commenting on the manuscript before publication and in particular:

Mariya Ahmed
Luke Anthony
Maninder Kaur Bains
Tom Barber
Liam Bickham
Emily Booth
Sarah Cain
Kyle Chapman
Cieran
T. Cutts
Lyndsey Duffy

Robb Hann
Liam Hughes
Kieren Moyle
Charlotte Naylor
Julia Pirie
Denise Stanton
S. Thackery
Laura Watson
Stacey Whiston
Aaron Wulls
Somiah Zafar

Become a Consultant!

Would you like to give us feedback on our titles before they are published? Contact us at the email address below – we'd love to hear from you!

info@barringtonstoke.co.uk
www.barringtonstoke.co.uk

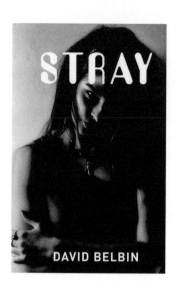

Stray

Even in a gang, she's on her own.
Stray's in with the wrong lot.
Can Kev save her?
Or will she drag him down?

Coma

Girlfriend in a coma.
A crash in the dark.
Todd's girlfriend Lucy is in a coma.
And now Todd's started seeing Jade.
But what if Lucy wakes up?

You can order these books directly from our website at
www.barringtonstoke.co.uk

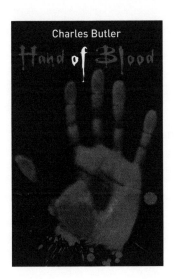

Hand of Blood
by
Charles Butler

Meg lost a hand.
Now she has been given a
new one.
A dead girl's hand.
But it seems to have a life
of its own
And it wants revenge ...

Mind-Set
by
Joanna Kenrick

Mark and Shaleem are
best mates.
But the bombs change
everything.
Will Mark stand up for
Shaleem when it matters?

You can order these books directly from our website at
www.barringtonstoke.co.uk